FRO

IDEA

— *to* —

MARKET

A Health Tech Entrepreneur's Playbook

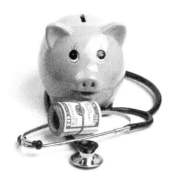

Drive Growth, Scale and Profit

FROM
IDEA
— *to* —
MARKET

A Health Tech Entrepreneur's Playbook

Drive Growth, Scale and Profit

VINEET AGRAWAL

Worldwide Publishing by
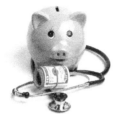 **Pendown** Press

PENDOWN PRESS

An ISO 9001 & ISO 14001 Certified Co.,

Regd. Office: 2525/193, 1st Floor, Onkar Nagar-A,
Tri Nagar, Delhi-110035
Ph.: 09350849407, 09312235086
E-mail: info@pendownpress.com
Branch Office: 1A/2A, 20, Hari Sadan, Ansari Road,
Daryaganj, New Delhi-110002
Ph.: 011-45794768
Website: PendownPress.com

First Edition: 2023
Price: US $14.99
ISBN: 978-93-5554-552-7

Contents

Acknowledgements

From the depths of my heart, I want to express my deepest gratitude to the remarkable clients whose experiences and challenges were the driving force behind the creation of this book. Their encouragement and faith in my ability to guide them through the unique world of healthtech have motivated me to pen this invaluable resource. Without them, this book would have remained an unrealized dream.

I am immensely thankful to Ms. Piya Seth and Mr. Adam Scott, the editors of this book, whose exceptional editorial skills and attention to detail have brought clarity and coherence to the manuscript. Their feedback and suggestions have helped me refine and improve this work beyond measure.

My appreciation knows no bounds for the invaluable feedback and insights marketing guru Akshar Yadav provided. His expertise, along with the outstanding subject matter contributions from Dr. Lavanya Rastogi, Dr. Benjamin Schooley, and Dr. Sue Feldman, have enriched this book beyond measure. Their collective wisdom and advice were nothing short of a guiding light during the creation of this manuscript.

To my beloved wife, Sonali Minocha, words cannot express my gratitude for the love, support, and inspiration you've bestowed upon me throughout this journey. You've taught me the true meaning of sharing and caring, and your unwavering dedication has been the foundation upon which this book was built.

I owe a debt of gratitude to my parents, who have been a constant source of inspiration and support throughout my life. Their unconditional love, guidance, and encouragement have been instrumental in shaping my values and beliefs, and I am immensely grateful for their presence in my life.

I must also express my heartfelt thanks to Dinesh Verma and the exceptional team at Pendown Publishers for believing in this project and providing their unwavering support throughout the publishing journey. Their dedication, professionalism, and commitment to excellence have been vital in transforming this manuscript into a published work.

I dedicate this book to all who have played a part in its creation, big or small. Through your support, encouragement, and belief, this work has come to life, and I am eternally grateful.

Introduction

*"Constantly think about how you could be
doing things better and questioning yourself."*

~Elon Musk

Mark's Dilemma

As I sat down for coffee with Mark in a bustling café in the heart of San Francisco, as the CEO and Co-founder of a promising medical device startup, I could see the frustration in his eyes. "You wouldn't believe it," he said, shaking his head, "My team just asked for an additional $50k to build interoperability. They claim it was never discussed!" he nodded as his frustration melted into sorrow. "I'm at a loss."

His words struck a chord with me, and I anxiously wondered how many other founders must face similar challenges in the digital health space. I pierced my lips to seal the dreadful truth. Unforeseen obstacles and escalating costs threatened to dismantle these founders' innovative healthcare solutions, leaving them feeling lost and overwhelmed.

The conversation moved at its pace as we walked towards Mark's office- a trendy startup hub filled with ambitious entrepreneurs. The modest, open-concept workspace buzzed with activity, reflecting the energetic spirit of a company on the brink of success.

I leaned forward and exclaimed, "Mark, developing health tech differs from traditional software development. The regulatory landscape, data sensitivity, specific industry requirements, and longer sales cycles add layers of complexity that many founders don't anticipate."

Mark nodded in agreement. "You're right. I wish I had known that sooner."

I looked at him and continued, "You're not alone. I've seen it time and time again with other founders. The complexities of digital health development and sales can be daunting, but there's a way through it. We need a comprehensive guide to help others like you navigate these challenges and unlock the true potential of their healthcare software products."

Mark's eyes lit up with hope. "That's exactly what we need," he smiled in agreement.

And so, inspired by Mark's story and countless others like him, I set out to write this book. A book that would serve as a beacon of light for healthcare innovators, providing them with the knowledge, strategies, and insights needed to overcome the hurdles they face in the ever-evolving healthcare industry. Together, we can revolutionize the world of digital health and bring life-changing solutions to those who need them most while emphasizing the unique nature of health tech development and sales.

Discover the secret to revolutionizing the digital health industry with my proven healthcare software product development framework. As a passionate and experienced innovator, I firmly believe that standardizing the creation process can result in a 10X increase in product sales, a 2X reduction in development costs, and a significantly faster time to market.

With 25 years of diverse experience in the digital health industry, I have a unique perspective on what it takes to succeed. I have worn many hats - as a founder of healthcare startups, investor in startups, and development partner to eHealth startups. This broad exposure has allowed me to fully understand the intricacies of digital health product creation and development.

With a proven track record of success, boasting over 300 million users, raised funding of 200 million USD, and an annual revenue of 500 million USD, I have cracked the code and developed a unique framework for creating profitable digital health products. Whether you're looking to develop a Health application, medical device software, or digital health solution, my roadmap offers a clear path to success.

This framework is unlike anything else and provides an unparalleled opportunity to learn from my experiences, moreover, avoid common pitfalls. Get ready to revolutionize your digital health product development approach and turn your ideas into profitable ventures.

Gain access to the insider knowledge and expert insights that have led to my success as I share the best practices for building secure, HIPAA-compliant, interoperable, and compliance-meeting healthcare software. This book is the only book that provides a comprehensive guide to creating a money-generating healthcare application. Get ready to transform your ideas into reality and change the digital health game forever!

The field of eHealth is rapidly growing and offers a vast opportunity for entrepreneurs and researchers to bring innovative products into the market. However, creating a successful eHealth product can be complex and challenging. There is a lot to consider, from researching and developing the product to ensuring that it complies with regulations and gains traction in the market. This is why we have created a comprehensive guide to discover the secrets of creating successful eHealth products.

Whether you are a founder looking to launch a new product or a health and wellness researcher looking to commercialize your research, this book is for you. This book will provide a step-by-step guide to help you navigate the complex landscape of eHealth product development and transform your innovative ideas into reality. Using the information in this guide, you can improve your time to market by 2X and build scalable and secure products that are high in demand.

One of the critical challenges in creating eHealth products is ensuring compliance with regulations, particularly HIPAA (Health Insurance Portability and Accountability Act). This law governs the handling of protected health information and sets strict standards for storing, transmitting, and processing it. Failure to comply with HIPAA can result in significant financial penalties and damage your reputation. This guide will help you to ensure built-in HIPAA compliance, not just a BAA (Business Associate Agreement), which is a document that outlines the responsibilities of the parties involved in a business relationship. With the guidance of this book, you can rest assured that your eHealth product will fully comply with all relevant regulations.

Another critical aspect of creating successful eHealth products is to secure funding. With sufficient funding, your product may make it to the market. This guide will help you gain faster funding for your development by providing the tools and strategies you need to secure your investment. In addition, you will learn how to create a compelling pitch, build a strong network of investors, and negotiate the best terms for your product.

Finally, this guide will teach you how to sell before developing. This strategy is essential in the eHealth industry, where competition and customers can be brutal. By selling before expanding, you can validate your product idea and ensure that there is a market for what you are offering. In addition, you will learn to create a minimum viable product, build a sales funnel, and smoothly close customer deals.

In conclusion, this guide is a must-read resource to create effective and efficient eHealth products. It provides a comprehensive and step-by-step approach to product development, from researching and developing the product to ensuring that it complies with regulations and gains traction in the market. By the conclusion of this book, you will have a comprehensive understanding of the critical elements to craft a successful digital health product. In addition, you will gain valuable insights into the strategies and approaches used by others in the industry and a clear understanding of how you can effectively lead your technology teams and outsourcing partners to achieve your goals.

You will be equipped with the tools and knowledge to gather critical client feedback, allowing you to make informed decisions and refine your product vision. Moreover, you will gain the skills to effectively communicate and market your product, even before its development.

By the end of this book, you will be equipped with a thorough understanding of the digital health industry, empowering you to confidently guide your team and make informed decisions about your product.

Are you ready to embark on this journey of discovery and transformation?

Join me as we unlock the untold secrets of digital health product development and revolutionize the world of healthcare innovation. Together, we can impact millions of lives and bring a transformational change in digital health.

Chapter 1

Healthcare Software: A Different Ballgame

"Healthcare is not a business. It's a complex system of people, processes, and technology that is designed to improve the health of individuals and populations. Healthtech products need to be designed with this complexity in mind, and they need to be able to integrate with existing systems and workflows."

~Dr. Robert Wachter

Professor of Medicine at the University of California, San Francisco.

Mike's Story: A Noble Endeavour with No Results

Meet Mike- a passionate software engineer living in the heart of Silicon Valley. He was inspired to initiate a monumental change in the world after supporting his mother's struggle with dementia. Despite Mike's unwavering dedication and his mother's best efforts, she often missed taking her medicines on time, causing further unwanted health complications.

Mike was determined to find a solution to this problem.

He worked tirelessly on a prototype for a medical adherence device and application to help people like his mother manage their medication more effectively. The feedback was overwhelmingly positive, allowing Mike a sigh of relief and hope.

With the support of friends and a small team, Mike launched his company and spent months researching, raising seed funding, and developing the first version of his product. Despite the enthusiasm he observed from the market, Mike soon realized that these developments needed to be increased more than these developments were needed. Instead, he needed to pay more attention to the complexity of the healthcare industry.

Hospitals, doctors, and other stakeholders had specific security, compliance, and integration requirements with existing systems. It took many months for Mike to improve his product and incorporate these features, but there was still time. The budget for development had surpassed expectations, and the runway was exhausted. As a result, investors were frustrated, and competitors had already launched better products.

Mike was devastated. All his hard work, passion, and determination seemed to fade. Feeling defeated and disheartened, he was forced to shut down the company and return to his day job.

The challenges and requirements of developing healthcare software differ from those of traditional software development.

The healthcare industry is heavily regulated, with strict security, compliance, and data privacy requirements. As a result, developing successful healthcare software requires a deep understanding of the industry and its specific needs.

Furthermore, the complexity of healthcare systems, the diversity of stakeholders, and the dynamic nature of patient data pose significant challenges for software developers. Ensuring the software is secure, interoperable with existing systems, and can handle sensitive patient information is critical.

In addition, the approval process for healthcare software can be long and arduous, requiring extensive documentation and certification from regulatory agencies such as the FDA. In addition, the development process must be meticulously planned and executed, prioritizing sufficient budget and resources for compliance and regulatory requirements.

Despite these challenges, the potential rewards for developing successful healthcare software are substantial. With an aging population and increasing demand for better health outcomes, there is a growing need for innovative solutions that improve patient care and outcomes. By understanding the unique requirements and challenges of the healthcare industry and approaching development with a focus on meeting these needs, software developers can create products that have a meaningful impact on people's lives.

The development and maintenance of healthcare applications are distinct from other software applications for several reasons. This section of the chapter outlines seven key aspects that contribute to the uniqueness of healthcare applications:

- **Regulatory intricacies:** Healthcare applications are governed by many stringent regulations, such as HIPAA in the US or GDPR in Europe, mandating strict adherence to security, privacy, and compliance standards for managing patient information and electronic health records.

- **Enhanced data security:** Healthcare applications process highly sensitive personal and medical data, necessitating more robust security protocols and privacy measures than many other software applications.

- **Uncompromising service continuity:** Even minor service disruptions can have severe consequences in the healthcare sector. As a result, healthcare applications must ensure high availability, fault resilience, and consistent uptime for reliable and continuous access.

- **Compatibility with medical equipment and systems:** Healthcare applications must seamlessly integrate with various medical devices, such as diagnostic tools and imaging machines, as well as healthcare systems like electronic health records (EHRs) and health information exchanges (HIEs). This requires specialized expertise and capabilities for smooth interoperability.

- **Support for informed clinical choices:** Many healthcare applications include clinical decision support features that utilize algorithms and data analytics to assist healthcare professionals in making evidence-based treatment decisions. This demands a comprehensive understanding of medical knowledge and strict compliance with clinical guidelines.

- **Exhaustive approval procedures:** Healthcare applications may be subject to extensive, complex approval processes that involve detailed documentation and certification from regulatory bodies, such as the FDA in the US. Successfully navigating these processes calls for meticulous planning and accurate execution.

- Ethical considerations: Given the potential for healthcare applications to directly affect human health and welfare, developers must address ethical concerns and prioritize patient safety, privacy, and equitable access when designing applications.

These factors highlight the specialized nature of healthcare application development and maintenance, which requires an in-depth understanding of the healthcare industry, its regulations and standards, and the ability to address the unique challenges that emerge in this complicated environment. These factors make developing and maintaining healthcare applications a complex and specialized endeavor, requiring a deep understanding of the healthcare industry and the applicable regulations and standards.

Though a comprehensive and applicable knowledge of the appropriate features is a prerequisite, successful healthcare application requires more than that. A unique, practical, and dynamic methodology is the next step forward. This book articulates a unique and ground breaking framework to crack the code of how Health Tech Applications should be built, scaled, and introduced in the market.

Introducing CHARISMA

The CHARISMA Framework redefines the development process, empowering you to create a product that transcends functionality, captivating users and stakeholders alike. This pioneering philosophy can unlock unprecedented acceptance, funding, and sales for your healthcare application.

The CHARISMA Framework revolves around the seamless integration of seven crucial components:

- Compliance-Driven Architecture
- Human-Centered Design (Sell first, build later)
- Analytics
- Research (Sell first, build later)
- Interoperability & Integration
- Security
- MVP (Minimum Viable Product)
- Assemble (vs building the ground up)

By cautiously weaving these elements into the fabric of your development process, you can craft digital healthcare products that combine functionality with exceptional user experiences. This unparalleled approach sets you apart from the existing competitors. This provides you with an edge over the others and significantly bolsters your chances of success.

In the following chapters, we will delve into the core components of the CHARISMA Framework, exploring each aspect in detail to provide a thorough understanding of crafting a digital healthcare product that transcends functionality.

Chapter 2

Sell First Build Later

Human-Centred Design | Research

"The goal of a startup is to learn what customers want and build a sustainable business around that."

~Steve Blank

The Co-founder of the Lean Startup Methodology.

Sarah's Monetizing Challenges

A Compelling Business Case

"My product is great, but I have a hard time selling it" I met a young and brilliant digital health entrepreneur named Sarah at HIMSS. She was passionate about using technology to improve people's lives and saw a promising future for AI in radiology.

Sarah spent several years developing an innovative AI-based radiology image analytics system. This one-of-a-kind system efficiently analyzed medical images and predicted the associated potential diseases. The plan was well received by doctors and received positive reviews, but there was a significant problem - who would pay for the analysis?

Insurance companies were reluctant to cover the cost as it was not a standard part of their offerings. As a result, patients were reluctant to prioritize an expense for a service that still needed to be voiced its relevance. As a result, Sarah was stuck with a fantastic high-demand product but needed a clear revenue stream.

Something needed to be fixed as she tried various strategies to monetize the system. Instead, the plan was shaped as an effect, desperately searching for the correct lock. As Sarah swedged a solution, she tried negotiating with insurance companies and pitching the system's benefits to potential investors. Unfortunately, nothing seemed to work.

Eventually, Sarah was forced to exit the company due to a lack of revenue. She was shattered to see her dream falling apart. But the future seemed promising with her optimistic attitude. The fire to improve people's lives through AI had some hope. Despite the setbacks of a rocky journey, Sarah continued to believe in the power of technology to transform healthcare and look for new opportunities to make a difference.

The story of Sarah's radiology image analytics system is a cautionary tale about the challenges of bringing innovative products to market. **Despite its potential to improve people's lives, the lack of a clear revenue stream made it difficult for the product to succeed.** However, Sarah's determination and passion serve as an inspiration to others who are working to bring new technologies to the healthcare industry.

The "sell first, build later approach" in digital health products refers to a strategy where a company begins selling its idea and a working prototype before it has been fully developed to generate early revenue or commitment to buy and validate the market demand for the product. The company then uses the revenue generated/commitment to buy from early sales to fund further development, raise money, and refine the product. This approach can bring several benefits to companies in the digital healthcare industry, including:

- **Fundraising:** By selling a product before it has been fully developed, companies can demonstrate proof of concept and show their product has commercial viability. This can be a compelling factor for investors, making them more likely to invest in the company and provide the necessary funding to complete development.

- **Increased Sales:** By offering a Working Prototype that meets the basic needs of their target market, companies can start generating early revenue and build a customer base. This can help them refine their product and better understand the needs of their target market, leading to increased sales over time.

- **Improved Product Development:** Early customer feedback is a valuable resource for companies, as it can help them to identify what works and what doesn't for the success of their product. By incorporating this feedback into their development process, companies can build better products that more effectively meet the needs of their target market.

- **Efficient Use of Development Funds:** By selling a product before it has been fully developed, companies can reduce the funding they need to complete the development. This conserves their development funds and allows them to use these resources more adeptly, as they can focus on the most important features and improvements.

This approach has become increasingly popular in the digital health industry and aims to bring innovative products to the market more quickly and economically. By selling the product before it has been fully developed, companies can validate the market demand, identify customer needs and preferences, and generate early revenue to fund further development.

For example, a company might launch a fully working prototype/ minimum viable product that provides a basic version of the product to early adopters. The company can then use the feedback from these early adopters to refine the product and add new features and functionality.

The "sell first, build later approach" can be particularly effective in digital health products. The regulatory environment and market dynamics can make bringing a product to market through traditional development methods difficult and time-consuming. However, it is essential for companies to carefully consider the risks involved, such as the potential for customer disappointment if the product does not meet their expectations or if development is delayed.

Know your customer!

Identifying your target customer is crucial in digital health products' "sell first, build later approach." To succeed with this approach, it is essential to identify customers willing to pay for a working prototype and provide valuable feedback for further development. Identifying the customer is a vast topic; it will take another book to cover it. However, the following approach is a good starting point:

- **Conduct Market Research:** Conducting efficacious market research is the first step in identifying your customer. This will help you understand the market and the needs of potential customers. To gather information, you can use various research methods, such as surveys, focus groups, participant observations, or secondary research. The data collected through this research provides insight into potential customers' needs and pain points. This helps clarify the actual need for your product in the market. The process of purpose-driven data collection is so crucial that it must be fulfilled by hiring specialized organizations, research universities, or experienced individuals.

- **Define your Target Customer:** Define your target customer based on market research. This involves creating a detailed profile of your ideal customer, including demographics, behaviors, and pain points.

Understanding your target customer will help you tailor your working prototype and marketing messages to their specific needs.

- **Identify Early Adopters:** Early adopters are customers who are more likely to be interested in your product and willing to pay for it before it has been fully developed. They are typically tech-savvy and ready to take risks, and by targeting early adopters, you can validate your product idea and gather valuable feedback for further development.

- **Build a Customer Persona:** Creating a customer persona is a helpful tool for understanding your target customer and their motivations. A customer persona is a fictional representation of your ideal customer based on the data collected through meaningful research. This persona should include demographic information, behaviors, motivations, and pain points. A clear understanding of your customer persona will help inform your marketing and sales efforts. This will further ensure that your working prototype meets their needs.

- **Connect with Your Target Customer:** Reaching out to your target customer is essential for building relationships and gathering feedback. You can connect with your target customer through online forums, social media, or networking events. This will help you validate your product idea and identify the features and benefits which are most important to your customers.

It's important to remember that identifying your customer is an ongoing process that demands ongoing market research and customer feedback. As you continue to develop your product, it is essential to continually validate your product idea and ensure that it meets the needs of your target customer.

Propelling Healthcare Software with Cutting-Edge Research

Research is a critical component of the business case for healthcare applications. It provides a foundation for understanding the needs and preferences of end-users, the state of the healthcare industry, and the regulatory and ethical considerations involved. Healthcare developers can increase their chances of success and build trust with end-users by conducting thorough research and using the insights gained to inform product development and marketing.

The business case for research in healthcare applications can be seen from several perspectives, including raising funds, selling more, safety, building trust, and marketing.

Raising Funds: Research can be critical in developing a healthcare application. **By demonstrating a thorough understanding of the needs of end-users, the state of the healthcare industry, and the regulatory and ethical considerations involved, healthcare developers can make a compelling case for investment in their products.**

This can include presenting data on market trends, user preferences, and clinical outcomes. This will also help outline the product's competitive landscape and differentiating factors. By demonstrating a research-backed solid business case, healthcare developers can attract the attention of investors and secure the funding needed to bring their products to the market.

Selling More: Research design can play a crucial role in fuelling the sales of a healthcare application. By gathering data on the needs and preferences of end-users, developers can create a tailored product meeting the needs of the identified target market. This can include adding new features and functionality that are highly valued by users, as well as improving the usability and user experience of the product.

Furthermore, by conducting clinical research to demonstrate the safety and efficacy of the product, developers can build confidence in the product among both healthcare providers and patients.

Safety: Safety is a critical consideration in developing any healthcare application, and practical research plays a crucial role in ensuring the safety of end users. Research methods to gather this data can include conducting a clinical study to evaluate the safety and efficacy of the product, as well as conducting technical research to assess the security and privacy of the product. In addition, healthcare developers can incorporate effective research to reduce the risk of adverse outcomes. This will help build trust in the users ensuring safety and security while using the product.

Building Trust: Safety and trust work hand in hand for their crucial role in the success of any healthcare application. Informing the potential or present users about processes of ethically and responsibly designing the product implicitly builds trust **by demonstrating a commitment to research and**

focusing on end-users needs; healthcare developers not only build trust with users but also increase the likelihood of success for their products.

Marketing: Effective research can also be essential in marketing and promoting a healthcare application. **By presenting the results of user and clinical research, developers can make a compelling case for the value of their product to potential users.** This can include showcasing the product's safety, efficacy, and user-centered design. It further highlights its unique features and functionality. By leveraging research to support their marketing efforts, healthcare developers can increase the visibility of their products and attract more users.

Several different types of research are involved in the development of healthcare applications. Some of the most common types of study include:

User Research

User research is critical in developing healthcare applications because it helps to understand end-users' needs, preferences, and behaviors. This research involves qualitative methods such as user interviews, surveys , and focus groups. By gathering primary data, which is directly collected from users, healthcare developers can identify the features and functionality that are most important to users. They can also observe the health application users' pain points and challenges.

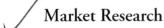

Market Research

Market research marks another essential aspect of healthcare application development. Not only does it provide information on the current state of the healthcare industry, but it also reveals critical data on the competition and the target market. Such research often involves using quantitative methods, such as market surveys and quantitative analysis of market trends. This includes data on the healthcare market's size, growth, and segments. With this information, healthcare developers can make informed decisions about the business strategy for their product, focusing on the target market, pricing, and distribution.

Clinical Research

Clinical research is essential for developing healthcare applications that involve medical decision-making and treatment recommendations. This type of research involves the study of medical treatments and therapies to determine their efficacy and safety. Clinical research results are used to inform the development of algorithms and decision-making tools within the healthcare application, ensuring that the product can provide accurate and evidence-based recommendations to users.

Technical Research

Technical research focuses on the healthcare application's feasibility and technical aspects, including developing new technologies, protocols, and standards that may be required. This type of research often involves collaboration with experts in fields such as computer science, engineering, and medical informatics to ensure that the product is technically sound and can meet end-user needs.

Regulatory Research

Regulatory research concerns understanding the regulatory requirements and compliance standards to develop and launch a healthcare application. This research focuses on reviewing relevant laws and regulations and consultation with healthcare law and policy experts. By ensuring that the product complies with applicable regulations, healthcare developers can reduce the risk of legal action and ensure the product can reach the intended end-users.

Ethical Research

Ethical research is focused on the ethical implications of healthcare applications, including privacy, security, and informed consent. This research thoroughly examines the ethical considerations for processing personal health information. This includes the collection, storage, and sharing of data. By choosing a responsible and ethical approach to developing healthcare applications, developers can help protect the privacy and security of end-users. This ensures the safety and security of the product, which results in being well-received by users.

The research output, including user insights, market trends, clinical outcomes, and regulatory and ethical considerations, serves as valuable input for human-centered design and prototyping. By leveraging research insights, developers can create products that meet end users' needs, resulting in increased adoption and better healthcare outcomes. In the next section, we will explore how human-centered design and prototyping can further enhance the success of healthcare applications.

Human-centered Design: Crafting a Prototype that Sells.

Human-centered design (HCD) is a design approach that prioritizes the needs, wants, and perspectives of end-users in the design process. When building a healthcare application, adopting a human-centered approach is essential to ensure that the product meets the needs and expectations of its users. A user-centered healthcare application will not only be more effective in meeting the needs of patients but will also be more likely to be adopted and used by the target audience.

This chapter will discuss the steps in building a human design for healthcare applications.

Step 1: Know your customer.

The first step in building a human-centered design for a healthcare application is to understand the needs and motivations of the people using it. This is the foundation upon which all subsequent design decisions will be based. Designers should research using potential user interviews, surveys, and participant observations to understand the users. In addition, we have covered the research part in the "Know your customer" section.

Step 2: Define the Problem

Once the team has gathered information about the needs and motivations of end-users, the next step is to define the problem or challenge that the healthcare application is meant to address. **This should be based on the insights gained from user research and framed in a way that clearly defines the problem and the opportunity for design.**

For example, due to a complex and confusing healthcare system, patients may need help accessing the required healthcare. The opportunity for design here may be creating a healthcare application that simplifies healthcare service accessibility and provides patients with the information they need to make informed decisions about their health. **This problem statement should guide the design process, and all design decisions should be made to solve the problem in mind.**

Step 3: Ideate

Once the problem has been defined, the next step is to brainstorm potential solutions with a cross-functional team that includes designers, developers, healthcare professionals, and representatives from the target user group. This stage is about generating as many ideas as possible, regardless of their feasibility. The goal is to spark creativity and encourage the team to think outside the box.

Ideation sessions should be conducted in a supportive and collaborative environment where the ideas and perspectives of participants are welcomed. The team should work together to build on each other's ideas and identify potential solutions that have the most significant potential to meet the target audience's needs.

Step 4: Prototype

Once the team has generated a list of potential solutions, the next step is to create prototypes of the most promising ideas. Prototyping is a low-cost and low-risk way to test and refine the ideas generated at the ideation stage. **The prototypes can be in the form of physical models, paper sketches, or digital simulations.**

Prototyping aims to create a tangible representation of the solution that can be tested with end users. This allows the team to introspect and make changes to the design based on the feedback received. For example, if end-user feedback indicates that the solution is too complex or challenging, the team may consider making changes to simplify the design.

A working prototype is critical for digital health applications because it serves several important purposes:

- **Demonstrates the Concept:** A working prototype helps demonstrate the concept and the product's vision before the stakeholders, investors, and potential users. This allows them to understand how the product looks, feels, works, and solves the problem it was designed to address.

- **User Feedback:** A working prototype allows users to share their authentic experience of the product's design, functionality, and usability. This feedback is invaluable for improving the product and ensuring that it meets the needs and expectations of the target audience.

- **Validation of the Concept:** A working prototype validates the product concept and allows the team to test and refine the product before launching it. This helps identify and resolve technical or usability issues before the product is released to the public.

- **Attracting Investment:** A working prototype can help attract investment and demonstrate its potential to prospective investors. This is especially important for digital health products, which may demand a significant investment for development and market launch.

- **Testing and Refinement:** A working prototype allows the team to test and refine the product, ensuring optimal performance and user experience. This helps to minimize risk and increase the chances of success when the product is launched.

Overall, a working prototype is a critical component of the product development process for digital health applications. It helps to demonstrate the product's potential, gather valuable feedback, validate the concept, attract investment, and test and refine the product.

Step 5: Test and Validate

Once the prototypes have been created, the next step is to test and validate the design with end users. At this stage, it is critical to ensure that the plan meets the needs and expectations of the target audience. The tests should be conducted in real-world environments and involve actual healthcare application users.

Testing can take many forms, including usability tests, which involve observing people using the prototypes to identify any challenges or frustrations encountered during usage. Surveys, as discussed, can be used to gather feedback from a more comprehensive set of users. An essential goal of testing is to gather feedback that can be used to refine and improve the design.

Step 6: Refine and Iterate

Based on the feedback gathered during the testing stage, the design should be refined and iterated to meet the target audience's needs. Refining and iterating should be ongoing until the design reaches its final phase and is ready for deployment.

It's essential to remember that human-centered design is a cyclical process that involves ongoing collaboration between designers, developers, healthcare professionals, and end-users. The goal is to create a practical, user-friendly healthcare application that meets the target audience's needs.

Building a human-centered design for healthcare applications requires a deep understanding of the needs and motivations of end-users, a focus on solving real-world problems, and an iterative design process that involves ongoing collaboration and feedback from the target audience. By following these steps, designers can create practical, user-friendly healthcare applications that meet the needs of the people using them.

By incorporating human-centered design principles into the development of healthcare applications, designers can help ensure that the solution meets the necessary compliances and regulations. This can help ensure that the answer is user-friendly, secure, accessible, and easy to use. This further reduces the risk of errors that could lead to non-compliance.

Pro Tips

1. Conduct thorough market research to identify potential customers, their needs, and their pain points. Use this information to tailor your product and marketing messages.

2. Focus on early adopters, who are more likely to embrace new technologies and provide valuable feedback to help refine your product.

3. Develop a clear and compelling value proposition that highlights your product's benefits and addresses your target customer's pain points.

4. Consider offering a working to generate early revenue, validate market demand, and gather customer feedback for further development.

5. Be flexible and adaptable, as market conditions and customer needs may change. Regularly reassess your target market to adjust the product and marketing strategies accordingly.

6. Build strong relationships with key stakeholders, including healthcare professionals, insurance companies, and potential investors. This can help you better understand their needs and secure their support for your product.

7. Continuously engage with your target customers to gather feedback, refine your product, and ensure it remains relevant in the dynamic healthcare landscape.

With these inputs and understandings, you can now move toward product development. This involves creating a comprehensive plan outlining how the product will be developed and materialize into the market. In-depth research on the potential competition, understanding the competitive landscape, and ensuring that all puzzle pieces come together - technical architecture, regulatory requirements, customer needs, and business case - should be part of this process. Doing so will give you a solid foundation to build on as you create your health tech product and substantiate a viable business plan.

Chapter 3

Compliance Driven Architecture

"Compliance is not a hurdle to be overcome, but a foundation for innovation. By designing for compliance, we build secure, reliable, and trustworthy products- qualities essential to success in today's digital world."

~Bill Gates

Developing a healthcare application requires in-depth knowledge about the specific needs of the healthcare industry and the numerous compliance requirements that must be adhered to. This chapter will guide you through a step-by-step process to create a compliant healthcare application architecture, ensuring your application meets relevant regulations and industry standards.

At times, determining the specific compliance requirements for your healthcare product can prove to be a complex task. As you progress through the stages of launching, marketing and implementing your product in various environments, new certification requirements may come to light. For example, deploying your product for the Federal government could call for FISMA certifications.

The core principle of a compliance-driven architecture is to ensure that your healthcare product is designed with the flexibility and foresight needed to accommodate current and future compliance requirements. To achieve this, it's essential to incorporate fundamental architectural and quality-oriented practices during development.

In the subsequent sections, we will discuss these leading practices in detail, covering aspects such as:

- **Understanding the compliance landscape:** Gain insights on the regulatory environment, industry standards, and relevant certifications to your healthcare product. Understanding the compliance landscape also demands you stay updated on the latest developments.

- **Adopting a proactive approach:** Design your product to address current compliance requirements while anticipating potential future needs. This may involve conducting thorough risk assessments, scenario planning, and regularly reviewing your product's compliance status.

- **Implementing modularity and flexibility:** Build your product with a modular and flexible architecture, which welcomes scope for seamless integration of new components or features as compliance requirements evolve.

- **Fostering a culture of compliance:** Encourage a culture of compliance within your organization, where all team members know the importance of adhering to regulatory standards and maintaining high-quality, compliant products.

- **Continuously monitoring and improving:** Establish active monitoring and auditing systems that enable you to track your product's compliance status, identify gaps, and proactively address any issues. This involves regularly reviewing your product's architecture, features, and performance to ensure ongoing compliance with the changing regulatory landscape.

- **Establishing a robust Quality Management System (QMS):** Implement a QMS to ensure consistent product quality and adherence to industry standards, regulatory requirements, and customer expectations. A QMS involves documenting processes, procedures, and responsibilities to achieve quality objectives and to conduct regular audits and continuous improvement initiatives.

You can develop a healthcare product compliant with current regulations and the dynamic compliance landscape by addressing these key areas. This will help you maintain a competitive edge and offer your users a reliable, secure healthcare solution.

Identifying Relevant Regulations and Standards

The first step in creating a compliant healthcare application architecture is to familiarize yourself with the applicable regulations and standards.

If you are building your healthcare software in the United States, there are several vital compliances that you may need to adhere to; these include:

- **HIPAA (Health Insurance Portability and Accountability Act):** This federal law governs the privacy and security of protected health information (PHI). Your software must comply with HIPAA if it handles PHI.

- **FDA (Food and Drug Administration):** In addition to food and drugs, the FDA regulates medical or health-care-related devices. If your software is a medical device, it is likely to be subject to these regulations by the FDA. The FDA has specific guidelines for software as a medical device (SaMD) and mobile medical apps.

- **ONC (Office of the National Coordinator for Health Information Technology):** This office is responsible for promoting the adoption of health information technology and is involved in setting standards for healthcare software.

- **HITECH (Health Information Technology for Economic and Clinical Health):** This federal law incentivizes the adoption of health information technology, including electronic health records (EHRs) and other healthcare software. It strives for the use of the most advanced healthcare technology available.

- **CLIA (Clinical Laboratory Improvement Amendments)**: CLIA sets standards for laboratory testing and applies to all laboratory testing performed on human specimens for health assessment or diagnosis. If a healthcare application performs laboratory testing, it may be subject to CLIA regulations.

- **ATA (Accreditation of Telemedicine and Telehealth)**: The ATA provides telemedicine and telehealth services standards. Healthcare applications that provide these services may be subject to ATA regulations.

- **CMS (Centres for Medicare & Medicaid Services)**: CMS provides funding and oversight for healthcare programs in the United States. Healthcare applications may be subject to CMS regulations if used with CMS-funded programs.

- **State regulations:** Besides federal regulations, some states have different laws and regulations related to healthcare software. If your product is manufactured in one of these states, you must comply with the state and federal regulations.

- **Other regional or industry-specific regulations:** Depending on the target market and the scope of your application, additional rules or standards may apply to your project. Examples include the California Consumer Privacy Act (CCPA) and the International Organization for Standardization (ISO) standards.

Once the relevant regulations have been identified, setting up a Quality Management System (QMS) is essential to ensure that everything is documented and that different versions are accessible. Establishing the QMS before development begins will also enable you to keep the necessary chain of thoughts to demonstrate an effective system with documentation ready to go if a compliance requirement arises. This will provide a solid foundation for your product development, ensuring that any regulatory specifications are met and that quality assurance is at its highest level.

Why is a QMS System required?

A Quality Management System (QMS) ensures that healthcare products meet customers' needs and comply with regulations. In this section, we will delve deeper into each of these benefits:

- **Meeting customer Needs:** The healthcare industry is focused on providing safe and effective products that meet the medical needs of patients. By implementing a QMS, companies can ensure that their products are highly qualified and meet customer requirements. A QMS includes software development, testing, documentation, maintenance processes, and managing customer feedback and complaints. By following these processes, companies can identify areas where their products can be improved and, as a result, make necessary changes to meet customer needs.

- **Product Continuity:** Software development project team members and partners may change. This can lead to a loss of knowledge and consistency in the product.

For example, a QMS can help smooth knowledge transfer while the product remains consistent, despite the changes in the development team.

- **Meeting Current and Future Compliances:** Healthcare products are subject to numerous current and future regulations. A QMS can help companies comply with these regulations by providing a framework for monitoring and ensuring compliance. This reduces the risk of regulatory penalties and improves the safety and effectiveness of the product. By having a QMS in place, companies can proactively address regulatory requirements and ensure that their products meet current and future regulations.

- **Attracting Investments:** Investors are often more likely to invest in companies with well-established QMS. This demonstrates a commitment to quality and a focus on meeting customer needs, increasing investor confidence, and attracting more investment. Companies with a QMS are better positioned to secure funding, as investors can see that the company prioritizes quality and is committed to meeting customer needs.

- **Reducing the Cost of Development:** Implementing a QMS can also help reduce the cost of development by identifying areas where processes can be improved. By highlighting inefficiencies and areas for improvement, companies can reduce revisions, improving their processes' efficiency. This can result in lower costs and faster time to market, which can provide a competitive advantage.

Keep it Simple!

As a healthcare product, having a well-defined and effective Quality Management System (QMS) is a prerequisite to ensuring the quality of your products and maintaining customer trust. It's important to note that there is no one-size-fits-all approach to QMS, and you can devise a system that works best for your company and its needs. In addition, a QMS should foster a quality culture within the organization, where employees or outsourced team members naturally perform their tasks efficiently and correctly, resulting in a safe and effective product, which are crucial aspects of a healthcare product.

The variation in QMS can be attributed to factors such as the regulations that apply to your company, the markets you want to launch in, and the size of your company. For instance, if your company operates in the US only, you may not need to comply with ISO 13485, an international standard; however, if you plan to sell in both the US and EU, you may need to comply with both Part 820 and ISO 13485. Similarly, a smaller company may only need a more complex QMS, while a larger company may require a more comprehensive system.

When implementing a QMS, it's important to start with the essential processes such as document control and records management, design controls, risk management, and supplier management. As your company grows and you move closer to manufacturing and product launch, you can gradually add other processes, such as CAPA and Complaint Handling. In addition, you are keeping the QMS procedures straightforward and Keeping the QMS procedures transparent and easy to understand, limiting confusion and contradicting procedures.

A QMS should provide clear and concise procedures that guide employees or outsourced team members in performing their tasks correctly, ensuring that regulations are followed, and that work is done efficiently and effectively.

In this chapter, we discussed steps to create a compliant healthcare application architecture, including understanding the compliance landscape, adopting a proactive approach, implementing modularity and flexibility, fostering a culture of compliance, continuously monitoring, improving, and establishing a robust Quality Management System (QMS). It identifies critical regulations and standards, such as HIPAA, FDA, ONC, HITECH, CLIA, ATA, and CMS, and emphasizes the importance of a QMS in ensuring compliance and meeting customer needs. By following these practices, you can create a reliable, secure, and trustworthy healthcare solution that meets regulatory requirements and maintains a competitive edge.

The following is what you should have at this point in the development of your healthcare product:

- Who is your customer?
- Who will pay for your product?
- The needs and desires of your customer.
- A working prototype

- Validation of the prototype
- Mapped compliance requirements for your product.
- A defined base QMS system.
- An understanding of how compliance requirements will impact the product's architecture.

Now we will cover two more topics that have a massive impact on architectural decisions- Interoperability and Security. The following two chapters will give you an overview of these topics and ways to build architectural decisions based on these requirements.

Chapter 4

Unlock the Power of Interoperability: Achieve Greater Funding and Sales Success

"Interoperability is the key to unlocking the value of health data. It is the ability to access, share, and use data across different systems and organizations. Without interoperability, we cannot realize the full potential of health information technology to improve care, lower costs, and empower patients."

~Dr. John Glaser

Interoperability is an increasingly important factor in the development of successful healthcare products. It refers to the ability of different healthcare systems and devices to work seamlessly together. This includes exchanging data, information, and messages between other systems and devices and using that information to improve patient health care. In short, interoperability enables healthcare providers to access and use the information they need to deliver high-quality patient care.

Business Case of Interoperability

This section will discuss the importance of interoperability in healthcare products from several perspectives, including raising investments, selling the product, reducing development costs, and meeting compliances.

Raising Investments

Investors are increasingly looking for unique healthcare products that have the potential to be adopted and used by a wide range of healthcare providers and systems. By incorporating interoperability into the product design, healthcare companies can demonstrate to potential investors that the product can be adopted by many users, which can increase the investment potential of the product. This is due to the possibility of interoperability to enable the product to be used by a broader range of healthcare providers and systems, which increases its potential market size. As a result, investors are often more likely to invest in products with significant market potential, increasing the likelihood of the product being successful and generating a return on investment.

Selling the product

Interoperability can also make healthcare products more appealing to potential customers by demonstrating that the product is designed to work seamlessly with other healthcare systems and devices. This can increase the probability of the product being adopted and used by healthcare providers, further improving the overall sales potential of the product.

For example, healthcare providers often look for products that integrate with their existing systems and devices and provide the information they require to deliver high-quality patient care. By incorporating interoperability into the product design, healthcare companies can show potential customers that the product is designed to meet their needs and can be integrated with their existing systems and devices.

Reducing the cost of development

Interoperability can also help to reduce the cost of development for healthcare products. By incorporating interoperability into the product design, healthcare companies can reduce the time and effort required to integrate the product with other healthcare systems and devices. This can result in significant savings during development, improving the product's overall finances. Performance. For example, suppose the product is designed to work seamlessly with other systems and devices. In that case, it may require little integration work, which can help reduce the overall development cost. Additionally, companies can reach a broader market if the product can be integrated with a wide range of healthcare systems and devices, further increasing the product's financial gain.

Meeting compliances

Interoperability is often a requirement of various healthcare regulations and standards, such as the Health Insurance Portability and Accountability Act (HIPAA) in the United States. By incorporating interoperability into the product design, healthcare companies can ensure that their product meets the necessary compliances and regulations, which can help to reduce the risk of regulatory fines and penalties. This is because regulatory agencies often look for products that can exchange data and information in a secure and compliant manner. By incorporating interoperability into the product design, healthcare companies can demonstrate to regulatory agencies that their product meets these requirements and can be used to exchange information securely and competently.

Interoperability is a critical factor in the development and success of healthcare products. By incorporating interoperability into the product design, healthcare companies can increase the likelihood of their product being adopted by healthcare providers, increase investment potential, reduce the cost of development, and meet regulatory compliance. Interoperability allows healthcare providers to access and use the information they need to deliver high-quality patient care. In addition to ensuring that information is exchanged securely and complies with regulations, it also helps create a more connected and effective healthcare system that benefits patients, healthcare providers, and the industry.

Healthcare companies need to invest in interoperability early in the development process. This can help ensure that the product is designed to meet the needs of healthcare providers and regulatory agencies. This may involve working with standards organizations, regulatory agencies, and other stakeholders to ensure that the product is designed to meet their requirements and standards. In addition, healthcare companies should consider the potential impact of interoperability on their product roadmap and plan to incorporate it into their product strategy over the long term.

How to build Interoperability in your product strategy?

Interoperability in a healthcare product can be architected right from the beginning by incorporating the following steps:

- **Defining goals and requirements:** Before beginning development, healthcare companies should define their goals for interoperability and understand the needs that must be met. This may involve reviewing regulations and standards established by regulatory agencies and consulting with stakeholders such as healthcare providers and patient advocacy groups.

- **Choosing industry standards:** The next step is to choose industry standards for data exchange and information sharing, such as HL7 and FHIR, that will be used to build the product. This helps to ensure that the product is easily interoperable with other systems and can be used by healthcare providers to deliver high-quality patient care.

- **Designing the architecture:** Once the goals and requirements have been defined, healthcare companies should design the architecture of their product to support interoperability. This may involve using APIs and other technologies to enable information exchange and designing the architecture to meet industry standards and regulations.

- **Incorporating security:** Interoperability must be designed with safety in mind, as it involves exchanging confidential or sensitive patient information. Healthcare companies should incorporate security measures such as encryption, authentication, and access controls into their product architecture to ensure that information is exchanged securely and complies with regulations. Maintaining user privacy and data confidentiality is vital in a healthcare product.

- **Testing and validation:** Healthcare companies should conduct thorough testing and validation to ensure that the product architecture supports interoperability. This may involve working with partners and stakeholders to perform testing and validation, which can help to identify and resolve any issues before the product is deployed.

Interface engines are commonly used to build interoperability in healthcare products because they can automate and simplify data exchange between systems.

Here is how they can be used:

- **Translating data formats:** Interface engines can translate data from one form to another, allowing different systems to exchange information using various data formats. This is essential for ensuring that information can be shared between systems that use different standards and protocols.

- **Managing communication protocols:** Interface engines can manage the communication protocols used by different systems, ensuring that information is exchanged securely and efficiently. This can help to reduce the risk of errors and improve the speed or ease of information exchange.

- **Monitoring data exchange:** Interface engines can monitor data exchange between systems and provide real-time data exchange reports, allowing healthcare companies to track and troubleshoot any issues that may arise.

- **Improving data quality:** Interface engines can be configured to validate data and ensure it is accurate and complete before exchanging it between systems. This can help improve the quality of data exchanged and reduce the risk of errors.

- **Scalability:** Interface engines can be scaled to support growing needs, allowing healthcare companies to accommodate the increasing volume of data exchange as their product evolves.

Interface engines play a critical role in building interoperability in healthcare products by automating and simplifying data exchange between systems. By using interface engines, healthcare companies can improve the speed, security, and accuracy of data exchange while reducing the risk of errors, ultimately improving the quality of patient care.

In conclusion, interoperability is a critical factor in the development and success of healthcare products. It enables healthcare providers to access and use the information they need to deliver high-quality patient care. Incorporating interoperability into product design can increase the likelihood of the product being adopted by healthcare providers, increase investment potential, reduce the cost of development, and meet regulatory compliance.

Building interoperability in a healthcare product strategy involves defining goals and requirements, choosing industry standards, designing the architecture, incorporating security measures, and conducting thorough testing and validation. In addition, healthcare companies must invest in interoperability early in the development process to ensure that the product meets the needs of healthcare providers and regulatory agencies.

Additionally, interface engines are commonly used to build interoperability in healthcare products, as they can automate and simplify data exchange between systems. For example, they can translate data formats, manage communication protocols, monitor data exchange, improve data quality, and provide scalability. In addition, interface engines play a critical role in building interoperability in healthcare products by improving the speed, security, and accuracy of data exchange while reducing the risk of errors, ultimately improving the quality of patient care.

Chapter 5

Security: Sealing All Loopholes

*"The health system is the most complex
human enterprise on the planet. It is also
the most vulnerable to cyber-attack."*

~Dr. Atul Gawande

Why is Security important?

The need for security in healthcare applications is becoming increasingly important as technology plays a more significant role in delivering healthcare services. With the increasing digitization of healthcare, sensitive patient information is being stored and transmitted electronically, making it vulnerable to cyber-attacks and data breaches. Therefore, implementing robust security measures in healthcare applications is critical to protect this sensitive information and avoid the many negative consequences of a breach.

- **Compliance with regulations:** Healthcare organizations must comply with several laws that protect sensitive patient information. For example, the Health Insurance

Portability and Accountability Act (HIPAA) in the United States and the General Data Protection Regulation (GDPR) in the European Union both have specific requirements for the protection of personal health information (PHI), as protecting user privacy and data confidentiality is vital in a healthcare product. Organizations that fail to comply with these regulations can face significant fines and damage to their reputation. By implementing security measures in healthcare applications, organizations can ensure that they meet these regulatory requirements and avoid costly penalties for non-compliance.

- **Attracting investment and customers:** Investors and customers are becoming increasingly aware of the importance of data security and privacy and may be less likely to invest in or do business with organizations that don't take these issues seriously. By demonstrating a commitment to safety and security, healthcare organizations can increase their chances of attracting investment and winning business from customers who value these attributes. This can be especially important for organizations seeking to raise funds, as investors are becoming more cautious about investing in companies with a high risk of data breaches.

- **Reducing legal liabilities:** Healthcare organizations can be held liable for breaches of sensitive patient information, including fines, legal fees, and damage to their reputation. Reducing the likelihood of a breach should be a priority in developing a healthcare product.

Implementing security measures in healthcare applications can help organizations reduce the risk of such violations and minimize their legal liabilities. This can include encryption, multi-factor authentication, and regular security audits to identify and address potential vulnerabilities.

- **Protecting the privacy of patient information:** Protecting the privacy of patient information is essential for maintaining the trust of patients and the public. Implementing security measures in healthcare applications can help organizations ensure the confidentiality of sensitive information and maintain the trust of patients and the public. This can include access controls to limit who can view or access PHI, data anonymization to prevent the identification of individuals, and regular monitoring for suspicious activity. HIPAA covers the law governing the patient's privacy and is the most critical requirement of any healthcare application.

The following sections will cover practical ways to implement HIPAA in your application.

Getting HIPAA compliance implemented in your application.

Achieving HIPAA compliance is essential in digital healthcare for several reasons:

- **Protects patient Privacy:** HIPAA regulations are designed to protect the privacy and security of patient health information (PHI). By following these regulations, digital healthcare applications can ensure that patient PHI is not disclosed to unauthorized individuals and is protected from theft, loss, or damage, all three of which can lead to fines and damage one's reputation.

- **Meets Legal Requirements:** HIPAA compliance is a legal requirement for healthcare organizations and business associates. Failing to comply with HIPAA regulations can result in significant financial penalties and damage an organization's reputation. To avoid this, it is crucial to pay close attention to the details surrounding HIPPA compliances during the development of your product.

- **Enhances Patient Trust:** Patients are more likely to trust digital healthcare applications that are HIPAA compliant, as they know that their PHI will be protected and not disclosed to unauthorized individuals.

- **Improves Data Security:** HIPAA compliance requires organizations to implement robust data security measures, such as data encryption, access controls, and security monitoring. By implementing these measures, organizations can improve the security of their PHI.

- **Supports Interoperability:** HIPAA compliance ensures that digital healthcare applications can securely exchange PHI with other healthcare organizations, which supports interoperability and improves patient care.

- **Facilitates Compliance with Other Regulations:** HIPAA compliance is often required for organizations that must comply with other regulations, such as the General Data Protection Regulation (GDPR) in the European Union.

In conclusion, HIPAA compliance is essential for digital healthcare organizations and should be a priority when developing your product. It helps protect patient privacy, meet legal requirements, enhance patient trust, improve data security, support interoperability, and facilitate compliance with other regulations.

To architect a software application that is HIPAA compliant, the following steps should be taken:

- **Data Encryption:** All PHI should be encrypted both in transit and at rest, using robust encryption algorithms such as AES-256.

- **Access Controls:** Implement access controls to ensure that only authorized users can access PHI; this includes user authentication, role-based access, and time-limited access.

- **Audit Trails:** To track PHI access and identify potential breaches, implement audit trails. Audit trails should include the date, time, and user responsible for accessing PHI.

- **Log Off:** Automatically log off users after inactivity to prevent unauthorized access to PHI.

- **Data Backup and Recovery**: Implement a robust data backup and recovery plan to protect PHI during a disaster or data loss.

- **Data Retention**: Implement policies and procedures for data retention and destruction to ensure that PHI is not kept longer than necessary and is correctly disposed of when it is no longer needed.

- **Security Monitoring:** Implement continuous security monitoring to detect potential threats and breaches to PHI. Security monitoring should include intrusion detection, vulnerability scans, and regular security audits.

- **Incident Response:** Implement a formal incident response plan to respond to potential breaches of PHI. The incident response plan should include procedures for responding to, containing, and mitigating breaches of PHI.

- **Staff Training:** Regularly train staff on HIPAA regulations and protecting PHI. Staff should understand their role in safeguarding PHI and the penalties for violating HIPAA regulations.

- **Regular Risk Assessments:** Conduct regular risk assessments to identify potential risks to PHI and to ensure the security plan is effective. Regular risk assessments should be conducted annually or more frequently as necessary.

By taking these steps and following HIPAA regulations, a software application can be architected to be HIPAA compliant and to ensure the privacy and security of PHI.

The following is what you should have at this point in the development of your healthcare product:

- Who is your customer?
- Who will pay for your product?
- The needs and desires of your customer.
- A working prototype
- Validation of the prototype
- Mapped compliance requirements for your product.
- A defined base QMS system
- Understanding of how compliance requirements will impact the architecture of the product.
- Interoperability considerations for architecture and database design
- Security and privacy considerations for architectural decisions

Chapter 6

Minimum Viable Product (MVP)

> *"The goal of a minimum viable product is to test your business hypothesis, not to build a product that customers will love."*
>
> **~Steve Blank**
>
> *The Co-author of the Book The Startup Owner's Manual*

Alice's Story: The Pitfalls of Ignoring Security

In 2019, I met a brilliant entrepreneur named Alice in Houston who had an idea for a healthcare application. She was passionate about making a difference in people's lives and wanted to create an application to revolutionize the healthcare industry.

Alice had a prototype of her application and a clear understanding of the compliances, HIPAA requirements, and interoperability requirements she would need to build the product. Still, she needed to figure out how to translate all these requirements into a tangible product. Instead, she was so focused on the functional requirements and creating a user-friendly interface that she ignored the non-functional requirements such as security and privacy.

I noticed that Alice had neglected to consider these non-functional requirements and warned her of the consequences. Still, Alice was confident that her focus on the functional requirements would be sufficient to make the product successful.

However, as the product was released, Alice soon realized she had made a grave mistake: the application users were concerned about the security of their personal information and the privacy of their medical records.

Additionally, the product could not scale effectively to accommodate growing user numbers, leading to slow performance and frequent crashes.

Feeling discouraged and defeated, Alice turned to me for help.

I explained the difference between functional and non-functional requirements and showed her how to balance both requirements to create a successful healthcare application.

Alice improved her product by focusing on security, privacy, performance, and scalability. The result was an application that was user-friendly, secure, compliant, and able to meet the user's needs.

Alice learned a valuable lesson from her experience, and her journey's story serves as a reminder of the importance of understanding and balancing functional and non-functional requirements to create a notably successful and effective product. By prioritizing the needs of the end-users and considering both types of conditions, it is possible to create a secure, compliant, and user-friendly product.

Functional requirements describe the specific actions and functions that a software application should be able to perform. These requirements are essential to ensuring that the software application meets the needs of the end-users and performs the necessary tasks effectively. For example, in a healthcare application, functional requirements include the ability to view patient records, schedule appointments, and manage prescription orders.

Functional requirements are essential to any software application. Understanding what the end users need and expect from the application is critical when designing and developing a practical solution for your product. This requires a deep understanding of the target user group, the specific tasks they need to perform, and the regulations and standards governing the healthcare industry.

Non-functional requirements, on the other hand, describe the attributes and characteristics of the software application that are not directly related to its specific functions. These requirements are critical to ensuring that the software application meets the needs of the end-users in terms of performance, security, usability, and other essential factors. For example, in a healthcare application, non-functional requirements might include security and privacy requirements, performance and scalability requirements, and data management and storage requirements.

One of the critical challenges in developing healthcare applications is balancing functional and non-functional requirements.

On the one hand, it is essential to ensure that the software application has all the necessary functionalities to meet the needs of the end users. On the other hand, it is equally essential to ensure that the software application meets the non-functional requirements to ensure that sensitive patient data is protected and complies with the regulations and standards that govern the healthcare industry.

Balancing functional and non-functional requirements requires a deep understanding of the target user group, the specific tasks they need to perform, and the prominent regulations and standards in the healthcare industry. It also requires a strong focus on user-centered design and understanding how to design practical, user-friendly software applications.

One way to balance functional and non-functional requirements is to prioritize the requirements based on the needs of the end users and the specific tasks they need to perform.

For example, security and privacy requirements might be the highest priority in a healthcare application. This is typically followed by performance, scalability, and functional requirements. This prioritization process helps to ensure that the most critical requirements are met first while still providing the necessary functionalities to meet the needs of the end users.

Another way to balance functional and non-functional requirements is to use an agile development approach, which allows for a flexible and iterative development process.

This approach enables the development team to continuously evaluate the needs of the end users and adjust the software application accordingly. This can help to ensure that the software application meets both the functional and non-functional requirements in a balanced and effective manner.

Here is a comprehensive checklist of non-functional requirements that you must consider when building your healthcare application:

1. **Performance** – response time, throughput, and scalability

2. **Reliability** – availability, fault tolerance, and recovery

3. **Security** – authentication, authorization, privacy, and data protection

4. **Usability** – user interface design, accessibility, and learnability

5. **Interoperability** – compatibility with other systems and data exchange

6. **Maintainability** – efficiently fixing bugs, updating, and adding new features.

7. **Portability** – the ability to run on different platforms and devices.

8. **Flexibility** – the ability to adapt to changing requirements and environments.

9. **Testability** – ease of testing and verifying the software.

10. **Scalability** – the ability to handle increasing demands and workloads.

11. **Compatibility** – the ability to work with other software, hardware, and technologies.

12. **Configurability** – the ability to customize and configure the software.

13. **Localization** – the ability to adapt to different languages, cultures, and regions.

14. **Internationalization** – the ability to support multiple languages and character sets.

15. **Availability** – the ability to be accessible and available for use.

16. **Response time** – the time it takes for the software to respond to a user's request.

17. **Throughput** – the rate of processing and handling data

18. **Fault tolerance** – the ability to continue operating even if components fail.

19. **Recovery** – the ability to restore regular operation after a failure.

20. **Authentication** – the process of verifying a user's identity.

21. **Authorization** – granting or denying access to specific resources.

22. **Privacy** – protection of sensitive information and data

23. **Data protection** – necessary measures to prevent data loss, corruption, or theft.

24. **User interface design** – design of the software's graphical user interface

25. **Accessibility** – the ability of users with disabilities to use the software.

26. **Learnability** – ease of learning how to use the software.

27. Compatibility with other systems – the ability to integrate and exchange data with other systems.

28. **Ease of fixing bugs** – fixing software defects quickly and effectively.

29. **Ease of updating** – the ability to make changes and updates to the software.

30. **Ease of adding new features** – the ability to add new functionality to the software.

31. **Cost** – total cost of ownership, licensing, and maintenance costs

32. **Supportability** – the ability to provide technical support and assistance.

33. **Documentation** – quality and availability of documentation and user manuals

34. **Backup and recovery** – the ability to back up and restore data in case of loss or corruption.

35. **High availability** – ensuring continuous and uninterrupted access to the software.

36. **Disaster recovery** – the ability to recover from catastrophic events such as natural disasters.

37. **Load balancing** – distributing workloads evenly across multiple systems.

38. **Auditability** – the ability to track and log user actions and system events.

39. **Performance tuning** – optimizing performance for specific use cases.

40. **Encryption** – the ability to securely encode and decode data for transmission and storage.

41. **Compression** – the ability to reduce data size for storage and transmission.

42. **File transfer** – the ability to securely transfer files between systems.

43. **Version control** – managing multiple versions of the software and its components.

44. **Release management** – planning, testing, and deploying software updates.

45. **Change management** – the process of controlling and tracking changes to the software.

46. **Configuration management** – tracking and controlling changes to software configurations.

47. **Resource management** – managing and allocating system resources such as memory and storage.

48. **Quality assurance** – testing and verifying software quality before release.

49. **Risk management** – identifying, assessing, and mitigating risks associated with the software.

50. **Compliance** – meeting legal, regulatory, and industry standards and requirements.

How to implement the non-functional requirements in your product?

Non-functional requirements, such as performance, scalability, security, and reliability, are essential in developing a healthcare software platform. These requirements define the system's characteristics and components and help ensure that the platform can meet the needs of its users.

To effectively incorporate non-functional requirements into the backend platform, they should be considered and addressed throughout the development process rather than as an afterthought. This includes defining the requirements early on, incorporating them into the design and implementation of the platform, and continuously testing and verifying that they are being met along the way.

One way to do this is by building a platform focusing on modularity and separation of concerns. This allows for non-functional requirements to be addressed at the component level, making it easier to test and verify that they are being met. Additionally, using established design patterns and practices can help ensure that the platform is secure, reliable, and scalable.

Another important consideration is ensuring the platform can accommodate changes and updates as users' needs evolve. This can be achieved using flexible and configurable components and incorporating robust version control and change management processes into the platform.

Building a solid backend is essential for the success and sustainability of a healthcare software platform. A backend serves as the foundation for the platform, providing the underlying infrastructure and support for the front-end user interface. It manages and processes data, performs complex calculations, and communicates with other systems and databases.

Performance is one of the most critical considerations in the design and development of a backend. The platform must be able to handle large amounts of data, perform complex calculations in real-time, and respond to user requests quickly and efficiently. In addition, the backend must be designed to scale effectively to achieve high performance using load balancing, caching, and database optimization technologies.

Security is another critical aspect of the backend, as it protects sensitive patient data and ensures the data's confidentiality, integrity, and availability. This requires implementing solid security measures, such as encryption, access controls, and firewalls, and regularly testing the platform's security to verify it is secure.

Reliability is also a crucial part of your healthcare application. It should be considered rigorously, as the platform must always be available and functional to meet the needs of its users. This requires ensuring your platform can handle an array of failures or errors and implementing disaster recovery and backup systems to minimize the impact of outages and data loss.

Incorporating non-functional requirements into the backend platform is a crucial step in ensuring the success and sustainability of a healthcare software platform. By taking a systematic and proactive approach to these requirements, your platform can be designed and maintained to meet the evolving needs of its users and provide high-quality, reliable, and secure healthcare services.

Front End Back End (FEBE)

The development of backend platforms is a critical aspect of software development that needs to be noticed and given more attention.

This is particularly true in the healthcare software industry, where the stakes are high, and the consequences of poor software performance can be significant. In addition, the complexity and scope of healthcare software products, combined with the need for strict regulatory compliance and the handling of sensitive patient data, make it essential for healthcare software companies to invest in developing robust backend platforms.

While it is impossible to determine the exact frequency with which backend platforms are missing from healthcare software products, this is a common issue that must be addressed. For example, healthcare software companies must prioritize the development of scalable backend platforms to ensure the success and sustainability of their products and meet their users' evolving needs.

It is a common mistake for healthcare startups to focus too much on developing the front end, leading some to neglect the backend platform. While a visually appealing and user-friendly front end is essential, the backend platform provides the foundation for the software product. Much like a sturdy house whose interior may be beautiful, this foundation is critical for functionality, scalability, security, and reliability.

Here are some of the potential consequences of neglecting the backend platform:

- **Limited functionality:** A backend platform is essential for managing and processing data, performing complex calculations, and communicating with other systems. Without a robust and scalable backend, the software product may be limited in functionality and struggle to meet its user's needs.

- **Scalability Issues:** The backend platform accommodates growth and increases data and user traffic. Without an adequate backend, the software product may struggle to scale effectively, leading to performance issues and decreased user satisfaction.

- **Security risks:** The backend is responsible for protecting sensitive data and ensuring the data's confidentiality, integrity, and availability. Without a comprehensive backend platform, the software product may be vulnerable to data breaches and other security incidents, putting the sensitive information of patients and healthcare providers at risk.

- **Reliability problems:** The backend platform is responsible for ensuring the reliability of the software product, and without this, the software product may be at risk of downtime and data loss, leading to decreased user satisfaction and potential harm to patients.

- **Interoperability:** Furthermore, the backend platform is also responsible for ensuring interoperability with other systems, which is crucial for the success of a healthcare software product. Interoperability allows seamless integration with other systems and databases and is essential for providing high-quality, efficient, and effective healthcare services.

- **Attracting Investment and Selling:** The salability of the software product is also impacted by the backend platform. A well-designed and implemented backend platform can demonstrate the software product's reliability and quality, giving potential customers confidence in its abilities and usage. In contrast, a weak or neglected backend platform can detract from the product's overall value and make it less attractive to potential customers.

Focusing too much on the front end and neglecting the backend platform can be a big mistake for healthcare startups. A well-designed and implemented backend platform is essential for a healthcare software product and should be a key consideration in the development process. Healthcare startups must prioritize the development of backend platforms to ensure their products' success and sustainability and to meet their users' evolving expectations.

Chapter 7

Analytics

*"We must use data and analytics
to build a more personalized and
precision-based healthcare system."*

~Dr. Dariush Mozaffarian

*The Dean of the Friedman School
of Nutrition Science and Policy at Tufts University*

Incorporating analytics into healthcare applications is essential for deriving valuable insights, improving patient outcomes, streamlining operations, and making informed decisions. A comprehensive analytics solution can help healthcare providers identify patterns, monitor performance, and optimize processes. This guide outlines the key considerations and steps to integrate analytics into healthcare applications effectively.

Define Clear Objectives and Metrics

Before implementing analytics, it's crucial to establish clear objectives and identify the metrics you want to track. These may include patient outcomes, resource utilization, satisfaction, or financial performance. Feel free to be specific about the goals you want to achieve through analytics, such as reducing readmission rates, optimizing appointment scheduling, or identifying at-risk patients. Setting concrete and clear goals is a great way to ensure analytics are integrated into your healthcare application constructively.

Collect and Manage Data

Data is the foundation of any analytics solution. Collect and manage data from various sources, such as Electronic Health Records (EHR), medical devices, wearables, and patient surveys. Ensure data quality by implementing data validation, cleansing, and standardization processes.

Data Privacy and Security

Healthcare data in the United States is sensitive and subject to strict privacy regulations like HIPAA. Implement robust data security measures, including encryption, access controls, and secure data storage. Additionally, ensure that data is anonymized or pseudonymized when necessary to protect patient privacy and data confidentiality. Therefore, it is important to maintain trust with your users by taking their privacy and security seriously.

Develop an Analytics Infrastructure

Design and build an analytics infrastructure that supports your objectives and allows scalability as your needs evolve. This may include:

- **Data storage:** Choose a solution that meets your capacity, performance, and security requirements, such as an encrypted database or a secure cloud storage service.

- **Data processing:** Implement data processing tools and techniques, such as ETL (Extract, Transform, Load) processes, to prepare data for analysis.

- **Analytics tools:** Select tools and platforms that meet your needs, such as Business Intelligence (BI).

To build a robust analytics capability in healthcare software, it is essential to consider the architecture implications that can impact your analytics solution's effectiveness, scalability, and security.

Here are some critical architectural considerations for implementing a robust analytics system in healthcare applications:

- **Modular and Scalable Architecture:** Design your healthcare application architecture to be modular and scalable. This allows you to integrate new analytics components easily and scale the system as your data volume and processing requirements grow. For example, a microservices architecture can enable various analytics components' independent deployment and scaling.

- **Real-time and Batch Data Processing:** Healthcare analytics often requires real-time and batch data processing capabilities. It would be best to design your architecture to support these requirements by incorporating streaming data pipelines for real-time analytics and batch data processing frameworks for handling large volumes of historical data.

- **Data Integration and Interoperability:** Integrating data from disparate sources, such as EHR systems, medical devices, and wearables, is crucial for comprehensive healthcare analytics. Design your architecture to support data integration and interoperability by implementing standard data formats, APIs, and data exchange protocols, such as HL7 or FHIR.

- **Data Storage and Management:** Choose appropriate data storage and management solutions to handle the specific needs of healthcare analytics. This may include relational databases for structured data, NoSQL databases for unstructured or semi-structured data, and data lakes for storing and processing raw data from various sources.

- **Security and Compliance:** Healthcare data is subject to strict privacy and security regulations. Incorporate security measures, such as encryption, secure communication protocols, and access controls, into your application architecture to protect user privacy and data confidentiality. Additionally, ensure your architecture supports auditing and monitoring to comply with HIPAA regulations.

- **Analytics and Machine Learning Frameworks:** Leverage analytics and machine learning frameworks that seamlessly integrate with your application architecture. Choose tools and platforms that support various types of analytics, such as descriptive, diagnostic, predictive, and prescriptive analytics, to address diverse healthcare use cases. For example, incorporate machine learning libraries and frameworks, such as Tensor Flow, PyTorch, or sci-kit-learn, to enable advanced analytics capabilities, including pattern recognition, anomaly detection, and predictive modeling.

- **Visualization and Reporting:** Incorporate data visualization and reporting tools into your architecture to facilitate the interpretation of analytics insights. Ensure these tools support interactive dashboards, customizable reports, and data drill-down capabilities, enabling healthcare professionals to explore and understand the data effectively. In addition, integration with popular BI tools, such as Tableau or Power BI, can provide a rich set of visualization and reporting features.

- **Extensibility and Customization:** Design your architecture to support extensibility and customization, allowing you to adapt the analytics capabilities to specific healthcare scenarios and user demands as needed. Implement flexible APIs and plug-in mechanisms that enable the integration of custom analytics modules, algorithms, and third-party tools.

Building a sturdy analytics capability in healthcare software requires careful consideration of the architectural implications that can impact its effectiveness, scalability, and security. By addressing these critical aspects, you can develop a robust analytics system that supports data-driven decision-making and helps improve patient outcomes, optimize processes, and drive innovation in healthcare.

Chapter 8

Assemble
(and Not Build From Scratch)

> *"The key to building great software is to assemble the right components and APIs. If you can do that, you'll be well on your way to building a successful product."*
>
> **~Martin Fowler**
> *Author & Software Engineer*

In the dynamic world of Healthtech entrepreneurship, efficiency and cost-effectiveness are critical factors for success. Building a Minimum Viable Product (MVP) quickly allows you to test and validate your ideas, as discussed in the previous chapter. One way to accelerate MVP development is by assembling your app using readily available components instead of building everything from the ground up. This is not only more time-efficient but can save valuable resources as well.

This chapter will delve into the benefits of utilizing pre-built components for your application, focusing on how this approach can expedite the launch of your MVP. In addition, we will discuss various software components and products tailored to Healthtech applications, exploring the cost of development versus the cost of the subscription. Finally, we will highlight strategies for replacing or upgrading these components as your app evolves.

It's essential to know that some outsourcing companies may discourage assembling pre-built components, steering you toward building the product from scratch. This approach may only sometimes be in your best interest, as it can lead to longer development times and increased costs. By understanding the advantages of assembling and utilizing existing components, you can make informed decisions that will benefit your Healthtech venture in the long run.

Advantages of using pre-built components:

- **Timesaving:** Utilizing existing components can significantly reduce development time, allowing you to market your health tech app faster.

- **Cost-saving:** Leveraging pre-built components can lower development costs, enabling you to allocate resources to other areas, such as marketing and customer support.

- **Improved quality:** Established components typically undergo extensive testing and refinement, ensuring high-quality performance and functionality. In contrast, building components from scratch may not guarantee the same high-quality performance or functionality.

- **Easier maintenance and support:** pre-built components often come with dedicated support and regular updates, simplifying maintenance and ensuring compatibility with evolving technologies.

Cost of development vs the cost of subscription:

While the initial cost of development for custom-built components might seem more economical, the long-term costs of maintenance, updates, and support can be significantly higher. In comparison, the subscription fees for pre-built components usually include ongoing support, updates, and maintenance, ensuring your health tech app remains up-to-date and compliant with changing regulations.

Replacing components over time:

As your Healthtech app grows and evolves, you may need to replace or upgrade specific components. To ensure a smooth transition, consider the following strategies:

- **Monitor component performance:** Regularly assess the effectiveness and compatibility of each component, identifying any that may require replacement or upgrading.

- **Evaluate alternatives:** Research and compare potential replacement components based on cost, performance, compatibility, and support.

- **Develop a transition plan:** Create a detailed plan for phasing out the old component and integrating the new one, minimizing disruptions to your app's functionality and user experience.

- **Communicate changes to stakeholders:** To manage expectations and ensure a smooth transition, keep your team, users, and partners informed about component changes. Communicating even small changes is one way to maintain a healthy, strong, and reliable relationship with all parties involved.

Software components and products for health tech applications

This section will explore various software components and products for health tech applications across different categories, including Interoperability, Search, Identity Management, Security, and Communication Management.

Interoperability:

- **Redox:** A cloud-based platform that simplifies EHR/ EMR integration and data exchange between healthcare providers, payers, and technology vendors.

- **Mirth Connect:** An open-source healthcare integration engine that enables seamless data exchange between healthcare systems and applications.

- **Health Gorilla:** A secure, interoperable platform that connects healthcare organizations, enabling easy data sharing and collaboration.

Search:

- **Elasticsearch:** A powerful, open-source search and analytics engine that can be customized for healthtech applications to enable efficient indexing and searching of large data sets.

- **Algolia:** A hosted search platform that offers fast, relevant search results and customizable ranking algorithms, it is perfect for Healthtech applications with complex data structures.

- **Amazon Cloud Search:** A scalable, fully managed search service that allows you to integrate search functionality into your Healthtech app easily.

Identity Management:

- **Okta:** A comprehensive identity management platform that simplifies user authentication, access control, and user management for Healthtech applications.

- **Auth0:** A flexible, customizable identity management solution that supports various authentication protocols and integrates with numerous third-party identity providers.

- **One Login:** A cloud-based identity management platform that enables single sign-on (SSO), multi-factor authentication (MFA), and centralized user management for Healthtech applications.

Security:

- **Aptible:** A platform that helps Healthtech companies build and deploy secure, HIPAA-compliant applications while automating compliance tasks and documentation.

- **Paubox:** A HIPAA-compliant email and file-sharing solutions provider that secures sensitive data in transit and at rest.

- **True Vault:** A data security platform that offers secure, HIPAA-compliant storage and management of sensitive health data.

Communication Management:

- **Twilio:** A cloud-based communication platform that allows you to integrate voice, video, SMS, and chat functionality into your Healthtech app.

- **Plivo:** A communications platform that provides APIs for voice, SMS, and telephony services, enabling you to add communication features to your healthtech application.

- **Bandwidth:** A communication platform that offers APIs for voice, messaging, and emergency services, allowing you to build custom communication solutions tailored to your healthtech application's needs.

Conclusion

Assembling a Healthtech app using pre-built components offers significant time advantages and saves on quality and maintenance costs. By carefully selecting and managing these components, Healthtech entrepreneurs can create a successful and sustainable app that meets the needs of both investors and customers.

Chapter 9

Launch

You have now laid a robust foundation to commence your product launch activities. By reaching this milestone, you have accomplished several critical tasks that pave the way for a successful market entry. These achievements included:

- **Identifying potential customers:** You have researched and pinpointed the customer segments that would benefit the most from your healthcare product.

- **Securing commitments for "agreement to buy":** You have garnered interest from potential clients, some of whom have expressed their intent to purchase your product once it becomes available.

- **A working prototype:** You have created a functional version of your product that demonstrates its key features and capabilities.

- **Determining and fulfilling compliance requirements:** You have recognized the applicable compliance standards for your product and ensured that it adheres to these requirements.

- **Implementing a Quality Management System (QMS) and documentation:** You have set up a QMS that focuses on maintaining consistent product quality. You also documented the processes and procedures necessary for compliance and continuous improvement.

- **Building a robust backend platform:** You have designed and developed a resilient backend infrastructure that supports your product's functionality and scalability and keeps your user's privacy and data confidentiality in mind.

- **Creating a Minimum Viable Product (MVP):** You have refined your product to its core features and functionalities, providing a foundation for iterative improvements based on user feedback and market demands.

- Having reached this stage, you are well-equipped to tackle the next set of activities that will propel your healthcare product toward a successful launch and sustainable growth in the market.

With this solid groundwork in place, it is time to focus on the following tasks:

- **Product validation through early adopters:** Engage with your early adopters to gather feedback, identify improvement areas, and validate your product's effectiveness. This process helps ensure your product meets the needs and expectations of your target audience, allowing you to meet user demands better.

- **Applying for certifications:** If your product requires specific certifications, initiate the application process.

Certifications demonstrate your product's adherence to industry standards and regulatory requirements. This can boost your product's credibility and marketability.

- **Maintaining the QMS:** Continuously monitor and update your QMS to ensure consistent product quality and compliance with evolving industry standards and regulations. This involves conducting regular audits, identifying areas for improvement, and implementing corrective actions.

- **Refining the product based on feedback:** Use insights from early adopters and ongoing QMS monitoring to refine your product iteratively. This approach allows you to address issues and enhance the product's performance, usability, and overall value to its users.

- **Planning and executing a comprehensive marketing strategy:** Develop and implement a strategic marketing plan to raise product awareness, generate leads, and drive sales. This may involve a combination of online and offline marketing tactics, including content marketing, social media, public relations, events, and more.

By diligently addressing these tasks, you will be well-prepared to confidently launch your healthcare product into the market. As you navigate the complexities of the healthcare industry, remember to remain adaptable, responsive, and focused while delivering a high-quality, compliant, and impactful solution to your users.

Managing the Quality Events

Managing quality events is a critical aspect of maintaining a Quality Management System (QMS) for software as a medical device (SaMD), as per the guidelines established by the Food and Drug Administration (FDA). A quality event is any occurrence that can impact the safety, efficacy, or performance of the SaMD product. Effective management of quality events helps ensure that the SaMD development meets its user's regulatory requirements and needs.

The following are critical steps in managing quality events in a QMS for Healthcare software products, as per the FDA:

- **Identification:** The first step in managing quality events is to identify the event and determine its potential impact on the SaMD product. This can be done through routine monitoring, testing, and feedback from users and healthcare providers.

- **Assessment:** Once the quality event has been identified, assess its impact on the SaMD product. This includes evaluating the potential risks to patients, healthcare providers, and other stakeholders, as well as determining the appropriate level of response to the quality event.

- **Reporting:** Quality events must be reported on time to the relevant stakeholders, including the FDA. The report should describe the event, its impact, and the steps to address it.

- **Investigation:** The next step is to investigate the quality event to determine its root cause and to identify any underlying issues or systemic problems.

- **Correction:** Once the root cause of the quality event has been identified, implement corrective actions to address the issue and prevent it from happening again.

- **Prevention:** The final step in managing quality events is implementing preventive actions to reduce the likelihood of similar events. This may include changes to the SaMD product, QMS, or additional training for users and healthcare providers.

Effective management of quality events is critical to maintaining a QMS for SaMD, per the FDA. By identifying, assessing, reporting, investigating, correcting, and preventing quality events, healthcare software companies can ensure that their SaMD products continue to meet the regulatory requirements and the needs of their users, all while minimizing the risk of adverse events.

Handling Customer Complaints

The Food and Drug Administration (FDA) regulates handling customer complaints in medical device and SaMD companies through 21 CFR 820.198. This regulation outlines the requirements for complaint handling, including the processes for receiving, documenting, and investigating complaints related to medical devices. You can adopt the same for your healthcare software.

Here are the key steps in handling customer complaints as per 21 CFR 820.198:

- **Receiving complaints:** The first step in handling customer complaints is establishing a system specifically designated for receiving complaints. This includes procedures for receiving complaints via phone, email, or other forms of communication and documenting the details of each complaint.

- **Documentation:** All customer complaints must be thoroughly documented, including the date of receipt, the nature of the complaint, and any relevant information about the device or product. Not only does registering complaints help with organization, but it can help you recognize patterns to improve your software. For example, if you get many complaints regarding a particular aspect of your software, documenting those can help you recognize a possible need for change.

- **Investigation:** The next step is to investigate the complaint to determine its cause and to identify any underlying issues or systemic problems. The investigation should include an assessment of the impact of the complaint on the device's safety, efficacy, or performance.

- **Correction:** Once the root cause of the complaint has been identified, the next step is to implement corrective actions to address the issue and prevent it from happening again. This may include changes to the device, complaint-handling process, or additional employee training.

- **Reporting:** Customer complaints must be reported to the FDA under the applicable regulations and guidance documents. This may include reporting significant complaints about adverse events or deaths and periodic reports summarizing the complaint data.

Applying for the Certifications

Undertaking the journey to obtain regulatory clearance from the Food and Drug Administration (FDA) for healthcare software products can be a complex and time-consuming process. Understanding the requirements, steps, and timeline involved in the application process is essential to ensure a successful outcome.

The first step in the application process is determining the appropriate regulatory classification for the SaMD product. This is typically based on the product's intended use, the level of risk it poses to patients, and the type of data it generates.

Once the regulatory classification has been determined, prepare and submit the appropriate application to the FDA. This may include a pre-submission meeting with the FDA to discuss the product and the regulatory pathway and a formal submission with detailed information about the product, design, and performance.

The timeline for the application process can vary depending on the complexity of the product and the regulatory pathway, and the workload of the FDA. Generally, the review process can take several months to a year or more and may involve multiple rounds of feedback and revisions. This should not discourage you from your product or its worth but should motivate you to improve it. You must remember that this is a normal part of the application process.

Throughout the application process, it is essential to maintain open communication with the FDA and be responsive to requests for additional information or clarification. Additionally, it is crucial to have a robust quality management system to ensure that the product continues to meet its users' regulatory requirements and needs, and demands.

Obtaining FDA certification for software as a Medical Device (SaMD) is critical to bring a product to market in the United States. The process can be complex and time-consuming, but manufacturers can increase their chances of success by understanding the regulatory requirements and having a robust quality management system.

- The first step in the process is to determine the regulatory classification of the SaMD. This will help to determine the regulatory requirements and the type of FDA review required for the product. The two main regulatory classifications for SaMD are Class I and Class II. Class I devices are considered low-risk and are subject to general controls, while Class II devices are considered moderate-risk and are subject to special rules in addition to the general rules.

- Before submitting a formal application to the FDA, it is recommended to prepare a pre-submission package. This package should include an overview of the product, its intended use, and any available data or information about its performance. This pre-submission package can help the manufacturer understand the regulatory requirements and any necessary or additional information required in the formal application.

- The next step is to submit a formal application to the FDA. The type of application will depend on the regulatory classification of the product and the type of review required. The FDA will review the information submitted. Be sure to maintain open communication with the FDA, as they may request additional information or clarification from the manufacturer.

- If the FDA determines that the product meets the regulatory requirements, the product will be granted regulatory clearance and can be marketed in the United States. However, manufacturers must continue monitoring the development and ensuring compliance with all relevant regulations and requirements. This may include ongoing monitoring of customer complaints, regular reporting to the FDA, and updating the product or its labeling as needed.

In conclusion, reaching the milestone of preparing for a product launch in the healthcare industry requires fulfilling critical tasks. These include identifying potential customers, securing commitments for agreement to buy, creating a working prototype, complying with regulatory standards, implementing a QMS, building a robust backend platform, and creating a Minimum Viable Product (MVP).

Afterward, focusing on product validation, applying for certifications, maintaining the QMS, refining the product based on feedback, and planning and executing a comprehensive marketing strategy is essential. To keep the QMS, it is critical to managing quality events effectively, which involves identifying, assessing, reporting, investigating, correcting, and preventing quality events.

Lastly, handling customer complaints is also an essential process that includes receiving complaints, documenting them, and investigating them to take corrective and preventive actions to minimize adverse events.

Chapter 10

To A New Beginning

As a healthcare startup founder, introducing a software product into the market can be daunting. The process can be complex and challenging, especially if you are new to the software development industry. However, with a solid strategy, you can minimize stress and uncertainty to increase your chances of success.

The healthcare software development process is multifaceted and can involve several key activities, including and not limited to product design, user testing, regulatory clearance, and ongoing compliance management. To ensure a successful outcome, it is essential that healthcare startup founders have a clear understanding of the requirements and steps involved in each of these activities and that they have a robust plan to manage them effectively.

As a healthcare startup founder, you have a unique opportunity to impact the industry positively. By taking the first step towards a successful launch today and turning your vision into a reality, you can help improve patients' lives and make a lasting impact in the healthcare industry. So, don't wait – act now and start your journey toward a successful healthcare software product launch.

In conclusion, you have reached the end of this comprehensive guide, designed specifically for healthcare entrepreneurs who aspire to create innovative healthcare applications. Throughout this journey, I have provided a step-by-step blueprint to develop healthcare applications that solve real-world problems, improve patient outcomes, and ultimately contribute to a better healthcare system.

Now, you have two choices before you:

Choice 1: You can consider the CHARISMA framework in this book and collaborate with your team or outsource the work to external partners and bring your healthcare application to life. The knowledge and strategies shared within these pages will empower you to make informed decisions, optimize resources, and create a product resonating with your target audience.

Choice 2: Alternatively, if you're looking for a unique opportunity to work closely with an experienced mentor who profoundly understands the healthcare industry, you can join me in a more exclusive collaboration. Given my limited bandwidth, I can only work with a few entrepreneurs with a genuine passion for transforming healthcare. By choosing this path, you will gain access to the following:

- **My expertise:** Benefit from my years of experience in the healthcare and technology sectors, enabling you to avoid common pitfalls and accelerate your project's success.

- **Industry insights:** Stay ahead with the latest trends, innovations, and regulatory changes that can impact your application's development and market positioning.

- **Network connections:** Leverage my extensive network of industry leaders, investors, and experts who can provide invaluable advice, support, and resources for your project.

- **Tailored guidance:** Receive personalized mentorship and coaching tailored to your unique needs, goals, and challenges, helping you make the most of your entrepreneurial journey.

- **Accountability:** Enhance your focus, motivation, and productivity by having a committed mentor who will hold you accountable and help you navigate the complexities of the healthcare industry.

Regardless of your chosen path, remember that the journey toward developing a successful healthcare application is challenging yet rewarding. Embrace the learning experience, remain persistent, and continue to innovate. The healthcare sector is ripe for disruption, and with the right mindset, tools, and strategies, you can significantly impact the lives of countless individuals.

I wish you the best of luck as you embark on this exciting entrepreneurial adventure. May your healthcare application be a catalyst for positive change and a shining example of what can be achieved when passion, innovation, and determination come together.

The future of healthcare awaits – it's time to make your mark.

Appendix A

Software Partner Evaluation Sheet

Here is a vendor valuation sheet that can be used to evaluate software vendors for digital healthcare product development:

Partner Information:

- Vendor Name:
- Date of Evaluation:
- Evaluation Team Members:
- Criteria:
- Technical Capabilities:
- Experience in developing healthcare applications:
- Technical expertise in relevant technologies:
- Ability to handle complex technical requirements:
- Quality of previous work and portfolio:
- Experience with integrations and API development:

Security and Compliance:

- Understanding of regulations such as HIPAA and GDPR:

- Experience in handling sensitive patient information:
- Security and privacy policies and procedures:
- Approach to data encryption and decryption:
- Approach to security audits and penetration testing:

Project Management:
- Ability to meet project timelincs:
- Experience in Agile methodologies:
- Communication and collaboration skills:
- Flexibility and adaptability in response to changing requirements:
- Quality of project documentation and reporting:

Cost and Value:
- Cost of development services:
- Cost of maintenance and support services:
- Quality of services for the cost:
- Flexibility in pricing and payment terms:
- Availability of additional services and support:

Partner Reputation and References:
- Reputation in the market and among clients:
- Availability of references and case studies:
- Feedback from previous clients:
- Quality of customer support and after-sales services:
- Reputation for innovation and creativity:

Scoring:

- Technical Capabilities:

- Security and Compliance:

- Project Management:

- Cost and Value:

- Vendor Reputation and References:

- Total Score:

This vendor valuation sheet can be used to evaluate software vendors for digital healthcare product development based on several critical criteria. First, the evaluation should consider technical capabilities, security and compliance, project management, cost and value, and vendor reputation and references. The total score can be used to compare vendors and decide on the best vendor for your digital healthcare product development needs.

If you are interested in getting a detailed technical evaluation sheet for your potential software partners, you can download it from https://wi4.org/ideatomarket.

Notes:

Printed in Great Britain
by Amazon

59731874R00061